enchanted Fairy House

By the Editors of Klutz

KLUTZ

Contents

What You Get....3

Make Your Fairy....4

Hair Salon....5

Forest Fashion....8

Fairy Home....10

House....11

Furniture....16

Decor....21

Make Your
Storybook....22

What You Get

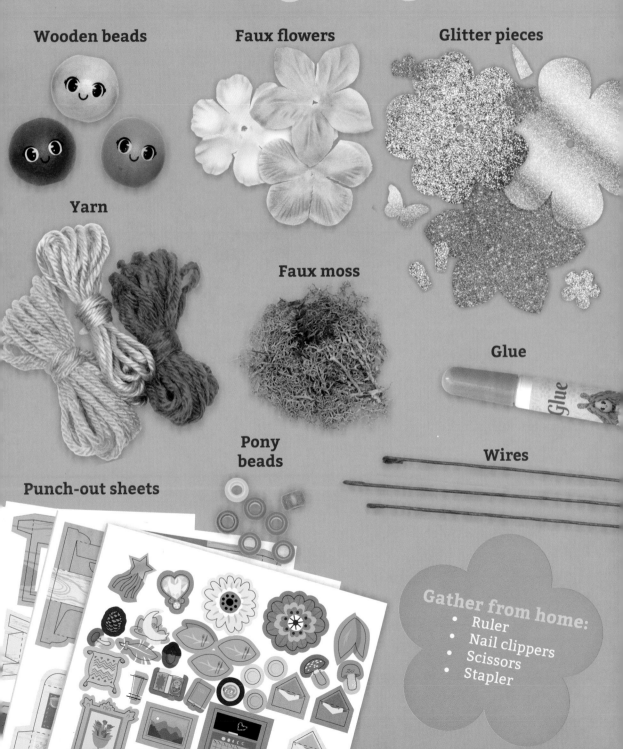

Wooden beads

Faux flowers

Glitter pieces

Yarn

Faux moss

Glue

Glue

Pony beads

Wires

Punch-out sheets

Gather from home:
- Ruler
- Nail clippers
- Scissors
- Stapler

Make Your Fairy

Style the hair, pick the outfit, and add the accessories!

Hair Salon

Choose a hairstyle before making your fairy.

Rapunzel

Purple or green yarn: wrap 5 times
Blue yarn: wrap 8½ times (use all yarn)

Pixie Cut

Purple or green yarn: wrap 5 times
Blue yarn: wrap 10 times

WHAT YOU NEED

Wooden bead   **Glue**   **Measuring board (from punch-out sheet)**

Glue
0.22 fl oz (ml)

Rapunzel Measuring Board

Pixie Cut Measuring Board

Yarn

Wire

FROM HOME:
- Ruler
- Nail clippers
- Scissors

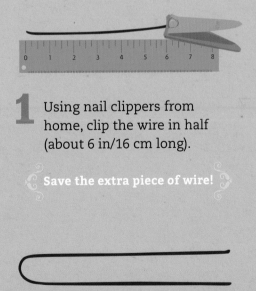

1 Using nail clippers from home, clip the wire in half (about 6 in/16 cm long).

Save the extra piece of wire!

2 Bend the cut wire in half.

5

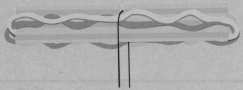

3 Pick a yarn color and hairstyle from Page 5. Line one end of the yarn up with one edge of the measuring board. Wrap the yarn around the measuring board the number of times noted for the hairstyle (one wrap = pulling the yarn to the opposite end, then back to the starting edge).

4 Slot the bent wire over the yarn and into the little notch.

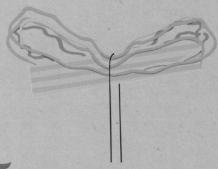

5 Gently slide the yarn off of the measuring board. Then remove the board so that the wire is in the middle of the yarn bundle.

6 Insert the two ends of the wire into a wooden bead and pull the bead up until the yarn fits just barely into the bead's hole. If you can't fit the yarn into the bead's hole, pull the bead up until it is right under the yarn.

7 Add glue to the bottom of the wooden bead's hole. Ask your fairy to do a headstand while the glue dries. **Let it dry completely (at least 2 hours).**

Put a small dot of glue on the end of each wire to keep the wire wrap from fraying.

Make a piece of fairy furniture (page 16) while you wait for the glue to dry!

8 Snip the loops of yarn.

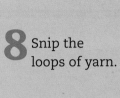

Optional: Untwist the purple or green yarn, and pull apart the strands to give the hair more volume.

9 Put a line of glue under the yarn to help hold the hair in place. Press the hair on top of the glue for a few minutes to let it dry.

Don't untwist my hair for this super cute style.

Try pinning back my hair with glue or experimenting with my hairstyles!

Forest Fashion

Play with faux flowers and glitter fabric combos to choose your favorite fairy skirts!

WHAT YOU NEED

Glue

Glitter fabric

2 pony beads

Faux flower

Extra piece of wire

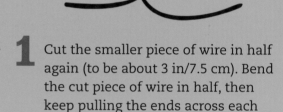

1 Cut the smaller piece of wire in half again (to be about 3 in/7.5 cm). Bend the cut piece of wire in half, then keep pulling the ends across each other to make a loop.

2 Thread the wire loop to rest below the head.

Optional: pull each end away from the other to tighten the loop.

3 Slide a bead, a faux flower, and a glitter fabric flower onto the wire to make a skirt.

4 Slide another bead to sit under the skirt, then fill the bottom of the bead's hole with glue. Ask your fairy to do another headstand while the glue dries completely (at least 1 hour).

5 Add a tiny line of glue to the top of the hair where you want to add the hair accessories. Press the hair accessory into the glue and pinch the hair around for a few minutes while the glue dries.

To keep the skirt down, put a dot of glue on the front and back of the fairy's legs. Fold the skirt down, over the glue, and place the skirt under a book overnight.

6 Glue a glitter fabric (or punch-out) wand topper onto the remaining piece of wire (about 3 in/7.5 cm) to make your fairy a wand.

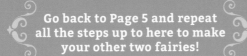

Go back to Page 5 and repeat all the steps up to here to make your other two fairies!

Fairy Home

Build and decorate a forest home for
your three fairy friends.

House

There's whimsy in these walls.

WHAT YOU NEED

Punch-out sheets

Glue

FROM HOME:
- Scissors
- Paper clips
- Adult helper

Optional
- Clear tape
- Jar

BEFORE YOU START: Punch out the house pieces and fold all tabs and fold lines to create creases.

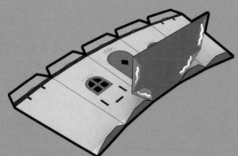

1 Put the yellow side (glitter side) down and fold the floor and the green tabs up. Squeeze a line of glue on the gray shapes on the bottom of the floor.

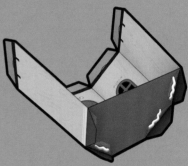

2 Fold the walls up around the floor and unfold the green tabs.

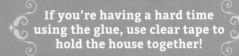

If you're having a hard time using the glue, use clear tape to hold the house together!

3 Press the green tabs onto the glue to overlap with the gray shapes. Stand the house up and hold the floor and walls in place to let the glue dry (around 10 minutes).

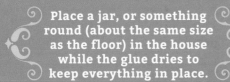

Place a jar, or something round (about the same size as the floor) in the house while the glue dries to keep everything in place.

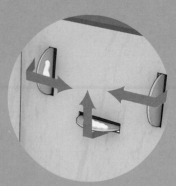

4 Punch out the mailbox or flower box. Fold the sides of the box in and fit the light blue tabs into the slots under the window.

5 Squeeze a line of glue along the tabs on the inside of the house, then fold the tabs over the glue. Hold in place for a few minutes while the glue dries.

Crafting requires a lot of patience, especially when there's glue. If you find yourself getting frustrated, take a break and come back to crafting later!

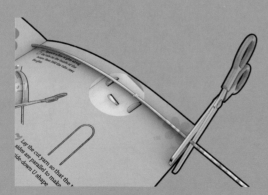

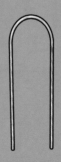

6 Hold one end of the yarn at the middle of the book and pull it across the page. Cut the yarn at the end of the page so that you have a piece of yarn about 7 inches (18 cm) long.

7 Lay the cut yarn so that the two sides are parallel to make an upside-down U shape.

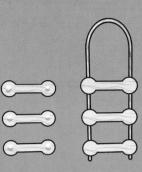

8 Place dots of glue on the round ends of the ladder rungs and press them onto the yarn.

9 Once the rungs have dried, hang the ladder onto one of the notches on either side of the house.

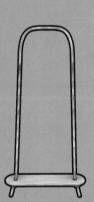

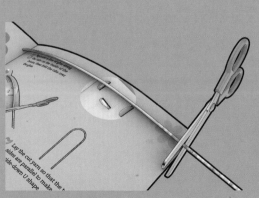

10 Cut a piece of yarn about 7 inches (18 cm) long, like Step 6.

11 Thread each end of the yarn through the holes on the swing and pull the yarn through. Tie a knot at each end of the yarn.

12 Hang the swing onto a notch at the top of the house.

13 Bend the roof piece along the fold lines to make a semicircle.

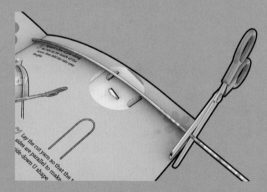

14 Pull yarn from the center of the book to the edge of a page and cut to make a piece of yarn about 7 inches (18 cm) long.

15 Thread the cut piece of yarn through the chandelier and pull the chandelier to the center of the loop.

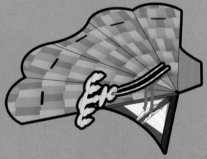

16 Turn the roof over and glue the ends of the yarn along the gray lines. Hold the yarn in place for a few minutes, then let the glue completely dry.

17 Fold the teal tabs on the house in. The half circles should stay straight.

18 Add some glue onto the gray tab on the roof. Hold the pieces with your thumb and pointer finger or use a paper clip to attach the tabs and let the glue dry for a few minutes.

19 Place the slots on the roof into the round tabs on the house. If you would like to glue the roof on, place glue on the house tabs before slotting on the roof.

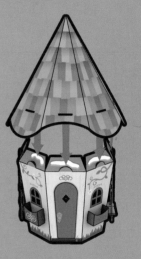

20 Use glue to attach flowers and a butterfly to the roof!

Furniture

Make your fairy house a fairy home.

WHAT YOU NEED

Punch-out sheets   Glue   Yarn

FROM HOME:
- Scissors
- Paper clips
- Optional: clear tape

Stove

Before starting, fold all of the tabs to create creases.

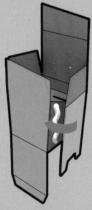

1 Smear glue on the gray tab, then stick it to the opposite side to make a box.

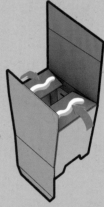

2 Fold the gray tabs in and add glue.

3 Fold the top tabs in, and add glue to the gray tabs.

4 Slot the bottom piece to close the box.

1 Add glue to the gray tab on the table base. Then fold it around to make a circle. Use a paper clip to keep the tab connected or hold it in place while the glue dries.

2 Fold the tabs down and add a squiggle of glue on top of them.

3 Then fold the top onto the glue. Turn the table base upside down to dry.

4 Once the table base has dried, place a dot of glue on top, and add the table top.

5 Repeat Steps 1–5 with the stool bases and stool tops to complete the table set.

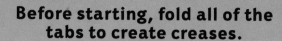

Before starting, fold all of the tabs to create creases.

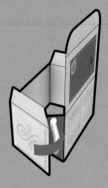

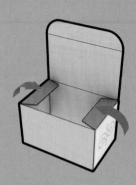

1 Fold the sides of the vanity to make a box, like Step 1 of the stove.

2 Then fold the gray tabs in.

3 With the top tab folded down, slot the top piece over the gray tabs to close the box.

4 Slot the mirror into the back of the box.

GNOME
Sweet
GNOME

Counter

1 Fold the sides of the counter down.

2 Crisscross the grooves to fit the two tabs together.

Artist Easel

Before starting, fold all of the tabs to create creases.

1 Fold the easel in half and fold all of the tabs in.

2 Place a line of glue on the gray shape, then attach to the other tab.

19

Canopy Bed

1 Fold the sides of the bed and the bottom gray tabs.

2 Add dots of glue to the gray tabs. Fold the bed down on top of the glue. Hold it in place for a few minutes while the glue dries.

3 Turn the canopy upside down. Fold the triangles and the pink tabs up.

4 Bend the creases on the canopy to make it hang a little, then rest it on top of the bed.
Optional: you can add a little glue to the top of the bed posts to secure the canopy in place.

Decor
Add enchanting embellishments!

Hang mini masterpieces with a dot of glue. Hold the artwork to the wall for a few seconds so that the glue dries.

Bend the green bottoms of the woodland creatures to make forest friends!

Place the flowers in their box. Then add some faux moss.

Fold the envelopes and place them in the mailbox for your fairies to find.

Use glue to add faux moss to the furniture to give it a forest-y finish.

21

Make Your Storybook

Follow the instructions carefully to put together the storybook pages in the correct order, using real book-binding techniques!

GATHER FROM HOME
- Scissors
- Stapler

1 Cut out the storybook pages. Make sure to cut out the number tabs as well.

2 Fold the pages in half, one at a time, so there is a crease down the center of your pages.

3 Stack the cut-out pages on top of each other so that the tabs are in order from smallest to largest (5 should be on top).

Flip through your book. If the page order still doesn't make sense, double-check Step 3.

4 Turn the book over, then staple two times along the crease.

5 Trim off the tabs, one at a time, with your scissors.

If your stapler doesn't reach, staple at the left edge of the **folded** book.

✂ **Cut along this edge** ↘

KLUTZ

Best Fairy Friends

Our story begins in a forest of green.

Where magical creatures are frequently seen.

Among all the trees lived three little fairies.

BFFs Merrie, Peri, and Keri.

They filled their new home with laughter and smiles.

And fairy-sized treasures in each of their styles.

The three BFFs held hands and agreed.

"When we work together, we always succeed!"

They gathered supplies and lo and behold.

They built a new home, even better than the old!

Each of them brought something special to add.

Their colorful roof made everyone glad.

Merrie was witty,
with bright blue
hair.

Her sparkly
skirt shimmered
and flared.

Her favorite thing
was to take
to the sky.

And play with
the birds and
the butterflies

Peri was playful and
kind like their grin.

Their long purple
hair always blew in
the wind.

They loved all the
flowers that grew in
the spring.

Whenever they
sniffed them, their
heart would sing.

"What do we do?"
asked a tearful Peri.

"Rebuild it, of
course!" replied
crafty Keri.

So the very next
morning, without
skipping a beat,
the three BFFs got
back on their feet.

Uh oh . . .
Snap! Whoosh!

The fairies flew out in
a flash, in a hurry.

They saw their home
falling, their hearts
filled with worry.

Keri was clever, and
crafty to boot!

She knew how to
build things and
make them look cute.

Her hair was as green
as a lush ivy vine.

Stars in her eyes,
she would dream
and design.

The 3 BFFs were happy
as can be.

They lived in a house
on top of a tree.

Then one rainy
night, while the
fairies were playing,
their branch started
moving and creaking
and swaying . . .